36 CASE

CW00671027

Beauty therapy
& electrology

36 CASE HISTORIES IN

Beauty therapy & electrology

Iris Rigazzi-Tarling

Hodder & Stoughton

A MEMBER OF THE HODDER HEADLINE GROUP

A catalogue record for this title
is available from the British Library

First published 1994
Impression number   10 9 8 7 6 5 4 3 2 1
Year   1999 1998 1997 1996 1995 1994

Copyright © 1994 Iris Rigazzi-Tarling

All rights reserved. No part of this publication may be reproduced or transmitted in any
form or by any means, electronic or mechanical, including photocopy, recording, or any
information storage and retrieval system, without permission in writing from the publisher
or under licence from the Copyright Licensing Agency Limited. Further details of such
licences (for reprographic reproduction) may be obtained from the Copyright Licensing
Agency Limited, of 90 Tottenham Court Road, London WIP 9HE.

Typeset by Rowlands Phototypesetting Limited, Bury St Edmunds, Suffolk.
Printed in Great Britain for Hodder & Stoughton Educational, a division of Hodder
Headline Plc, 338 Euston Road, London NWI 3BH by Cox & Wyman Ltd, Reading.

For my husband Nicholas and my daughter Alexandra

CONTENTS

ACKNOWLEDGEMENTS

I would like to thank the following therapists for submitting case studies for inclusion in this book:

Christine Collyer	UK
Amanda Dunn	UK
Ger Egan	UK
Sajvinder Jhally	UK
Danné Montague-King	USA
June Massie	UK
Christine Shaw	Spain
Valerie Teubes	South Africa
Carole Warren	UK

I would also like to thank everyone who has contributed to this book – in particular my dear friend Doris Bunce for typing the manuscript.

Photographs on the front cover by courtesy of Health & Beauty Salon/Ionithermie Ltd. (Energie Marine).

INTRODUCTION

36 Case Histories in Beauty Therapy and Electrology provides examples of a variety of conditions and problems which affect the individual. They are intended to make interesting reading, to widen the reader's horizons in some instances, and to remind all of us involved in beauty therapy and electrology how important our work is. It is apparent on reading these studies that many people have been helped in a variety of ways, both physically and psychologically, by having these treatments.

Where it has been available, important background detail has been provided. The client record format has not been included because of its length. However, an example of a relatively detailed client consultation checklist is given for the reader's reference. A 'specific points' checklist is also included as a reminder that these points can be major contributing factors in assessing a skin/hair problem.

In all the studies I have specified 'points to check'. These should be considered priority areas and any changes should be noted. We have all experienced situations where, as treatment develops, clients reveal additional background information that they have forgotten earlier. This information may be vital in ensuring an accurate *ongoing* assessment of the problem.

Remember that studying the whole person is of paramount importance with any problem. We are increasingly aware of the effects of stress and a busy lifestyle on our own bodies – similarly we must consider these points in our client consultations, to enable us to offer the best treatment.

HOW TO USE THIS BOOK

In order for the reader to gain full benefit from reading this book, the case histories have been listed

- by age
- by problem

Further information on specialist treatments has also been included at the back of the book, for your reference.

Notes

- References are not made to a specific brand of product, only a type of product (e.g. a French product for diffusing redness; a biological mask).

- Biological exfoliation (peeling) is referred to as a general term.

- Essential oils (aromatherapy), when used, have been added to a carrier oil and conform to the internationally recognised formulae, unless otherwise stated (e.g. weakened – half-strength).

- Specialist treatments have been highlighted in the relevant case histories and an explanation of these treatments appears separately at the end of the book.

CASE HISTORIES GROUPED BY AGE

Under 20

Case history 1	Fay
Case history 2	Paul
Case history 3	Avril
Case history 4	Christine

20–30

Case history 5	May
Case history 6	Gary
Case history 7	Mia
Case history 8	Jim
Case history 9	Pete
Case history 10	Frances
Case history 11	Vicky
Case history 12	Melanie
Case history 13	Susan

31–40

Case history 14	Marisa
Case history 15	Tim
Case history 16	Jane
Case history 17	Simon
Case history 18	Jo
Case history 19	Christie
Case history 20	Louise

41–50

Case history 21	Mary
Case history 22	Ellie
Case history 23	Denise
Case history 24	Emma
Case history 25	June
Case history 26	Helen

51–60

Case history 27	Abbie
Case history 28	Donna
Case history 29	Tessa
Case history 30	Tricia
Case history 31	Elise
Case history 32	Ingrid
Case history 33	Irene

61 and over

Case history 34	Rosie
Case history 35	Kim
Case history 36	Jean

CASE HISTORIES GROUPED BY PROBLEM TYPE

Hair-growth problems: face and body

Case history 3	Avril
Case history 5	May
Case history 7	Mia
Case history 9	Pete
Case history 14	Marisa
Case history 15	Tim
Case history 24	Emma
Case history 35	Kim

Hair-growth problems: upper face and head

Case history 2	Paul
Case history 6	Gary
Case history 8	Jim
Case history 17	Simon

Hair-growth problems: lower face and neck

Case history 11	Vicky
Case history 19	Christie
Case history 21	Mary
Case history 22	Ellie
Case history 25	June
Case history 29	Tessa

Acne and post-acne problems

Case history 1	Fay
Case history 10	Frances
Case history 16	Jane
Case history 18	Jo
Case history 26	Helen

Pigmentation problems

Case history 13   Susan
Case history 23   Denise
Case history 33   Irene

Sensitive-skin problems

Case history 4   Christine
Case history 12   Melanie
Case history 20   Louise
Case history 27   Abbie
Case history 28   Donna

Mature-skin problems

Case history 30   Tricia
Case history 31   Elise
Case history 32   Ingrid
Case history 34   Rosie
Case history 36   Jean

CONSULTATION CHECKLISTS

GENERAL CHECKLIST

PERSONAL DETAILS

name ....
address ....
telephone number ....
doctor's name and address ....
height ....
weight ....
age group ....
marital status ....
children ....
general health ....
recent operations ....

MEDICAL HISTORY

Circulatory conditions
e.g. high blood pressure
      low blood pressure
      angina
      thrombosis
      varicose veins

Respiratory conditions
e.g. asthma
      hayfever
      bronchitis
      sinusitis

Neurological conditions
e.g. epilepsy
paralysis
nervous tension
neuralgia

Digestive conditions
e.g. constipation
diarrhoea
hiatus hernia
gallstones

Skeletal conditions
e.g. fractures
kyphosis
scoliosis
lordosis
osteoarthritis

Renal/urinary conditions
e.g. kidney infections
kidney stones
urinary infections
cystitis
fluid retention

Endocrine conditions
e.g. exophthalmic goitre
Cushing's syndrome
diabetes
abnormal hair growth

Gynaecological conditions
e.g. menopause
pregnancy
ovarian cyst
pre-menstrual tension

Muscular conditions

e.g. fibrositis
      torticollis
      cramp
      rheumatism

Medication

e.g. contraceptive pill
      high blood pressure pills

Hereditary conditions

e.g. circulatory disorders
      abnormal hair growth

DIET

e.g. varied
      regular meals/snacks
      protein
      carbohydrate
      fat – high animal
          – high dairy
      vegetables/fruit
      fluid intake
      water intake
      alcohol
      sugar
      vegetarian
      balanced diet

LIFESTYLE

Work

e.g. type
      active
      sedentary
      environment

Relaxation
e.g. exercise pattern
hobbies

Habits
e.g. smoker

Emotional problems
e.g. depression

Stress level
e.g. scale 1–10
causes

Sleep pattern
e.g. constant
disturbed
insomnia

ANY OTHER INFORMATION

COMMENTS

SKIN ANALYSIS

e.g. texture
colour
tone/elasticity
blemishes
broken capillaries
dehydration
wrinkles
comedones
pigmentation
scarred
sun-damaged
congested

inflamed
reactive – heat
     – cold
healing time

Skin abnormalities
e.g. congenital
    acquired

Skin type
e.g. normal
    oily
    dry
    combination
    sensitive
    problem
    young
    mature

Homecare routine
e.g. products used

Skin disorders
e.g. acne vulgaris
    acne rosacea
    dermatitis
    eczema
    urticaria
    skin cancer
    herpes simplex
    psoriasis

Allergies
e.g. food
    environment
    medication

EPILATION ANALYSIS

(in conjunction with earlier information)

Previous epilation

Previous results

Hair growth history
e.g. since puberty

Hair growth situation
e.g. chin
  lip
  neck
  eyebrows

Hair growth type
e.g. dense
  fine
  strong

All consultations require:
- record of contra-indications
- treatment plan
- follow-up
- record of session
- homecare advice/routine
- suggestions
- any other information
- client consent
- therapist's signature

Specific points checklist

The following personal, medical and environmental factors must always be checked when treating a client's skin.

GENERAL HEALTH

MEDICAL HISTORY

- circulatory conditions
- neurological conditions
- endocrine conditions
- respiratory conditions
- gynaecological conditions
- digestive conditions
- skeletal conditions
- renal/urinary conditions

HEREDITARY PROBLEMS

SPECIFIC HEALTH PROBLEMS

- menstruation
- menopause
- ovarian problems
- pregnancy
- asthma
- pre-menstrual tension
- smoker

SKIN ANALYSIS

SPECIFIC SKIN PROBLEMS

- dermatitis
- eczema
- allergies
- products

MEDICATION

- steroids
- oral contraceptives
- hormone replacement therapy
- antibiotics
- high blood pressure
- anti-histamines

DIET

- vegetarian
- high intake of animal fats
- high intake of dairy products
- nutritionally unbalanced
- high sugar intake
- alcohol consumption

STRESS LEVEL

LIFESTYLE

- eating patterns
- sleeping patterns
- working pattern
- exercise pattern

Under 20

CASE HISTORY 1

Fay

Client   Fay – female – Caucasian –
                        English

Age   16

Presenting problem acne vulgaris – advanced

Previous history and medical history

The acne had started with puberty – aged 12. It had become progressively
worse and medical attention had been advised. Treatment with antibiotics
and a cleansing solution had been given for six months. This was then
terminated and the client was told the acne would subside. The condition
returned and apparently advanced quickly. The client investigated beauty
therapy.

The client had a varied diet, but sometimes this relied on convenience food.
She was taking no medication and had not had any serious health disorders
or recent operations.

Points to check

- General health
- Endocrine system/hormones
- Medication
- Diet (high dairy/animal fats, high sugar)

Assessment of situation

The client had cysts on her face, chest and back. The skin was excessively
oily, with inflamed pustules, whiteheads, blackheads, and hardened scarred
areas. She had no real cleansing routine and was always trying new
commercial products in an attempt to find something that would work.

*T*reatment plan

1 Once a week for three weeks.
2 Once a month – ongoing.
3 Homecare – daily cleansing routine, daily record of food intake and skin's appearance.

The client started to keep a notebook of everything she ate. She also recorded the state of her skin every morning and evening, her stress level from one to ten, and her monthly cycle.

A cleansing routine was established, using a mild cleanser and toner (camphor) at least twice a day. A daily kaolin-based mask was used and comedones were removed, where possible, using only a comedone extractor.

The treatment given initially, according to the client's financial situation, was once every week for three weeks, then once a month. This consisted of desincrustation solution (no electrical current required), deep cleansing, removal of any comedones and biological exfoliation. The client's skin looked consistently softer, brighter and clearer after treatment.

It was easy to monitor progress when the client was having weekly treatments. When the treatments were monthly, it was necessary for the client to be very accurate in her daily skin assessment. The client observed a gradual change in oiliness and the appearance of pustules in the week prior to her monthly period. She also observed changes in her skin (i.e. red lumps and patches) the day after she ate chocolate. The client's daily record of eating showed a high fat intake in the form of crisps, nuts and pastry. Chocolate was eliminated from her diet, though some sweets were substituted. Fat intake, in the above form, was restricted. There was a noticeable improvement in the appearance of the skin and the inflammatory patches were reduced.

After three months, the cysts and pustules were also improved. Biological exfoliation improved the texture of the skin. There were still regular outbursts of 'spots' before the monthly cycle, but these were located mainly down the centre panel and jawline. The daily records of diet and appearance were invaluable in monitoring changes in the skin. Any radical change of diet (e.g. at Christmas, when mince pies and rich food were eaten) brought about inflamed skin.

*R*esults and follow-up

After 12 months, noticeable changes had taken place. These included improved skin texture, reduction in pustules, blackheads and inflammation, and reduction of scar tissue. Within 20 months there was no acne, no scars, and the skin was balanced with a 'normal' appearance.

There were many factors involved in this client's condition and the daily monitoring of her skin and diet taught her a considerable amount about her health, body and well-being. Her psychological state improved because she felt she was doing something positive in monitoring her skin reactions.

CASE HISTORY 2

Paul

Client   Paul – male – Asian
Age   17
Presenting problem   coarse hair above eyebrows on
                                    each side of forehead

Previous history and medical history

The client was a highly intelligent student who, over the last few years, had become increasingly embarrassed by his facial hair.

When he was a toddler, his head had been shaved (once only) as was the custom in his religion. Whether this affected his hair growth is difficult to assess. He wore the hair on top of his head quite long, but this was not the same as the hair on his forehead, which was coarse and stubbly. He had plucked the hair, waxed it and, more recently, had bought a home electrolysis kit from a chemist. The hair stubble was unruly and irregular.

His health was good and he was extremely fit and enjoyed sport. He did suffer with asthma as a child, but this was no longer a problem.

The client did not wish to have treatment near to where he lived, for fear of people seeing him and finding out. He was extremely self-conscious. His father knew the therapist and brought Paul to see her as she practises out of his area. He was unable to have treatment regularly because of his school and sport commitments, but he chose to have treatments in the Easter and Summer vacations.

Points to check

- Skin healing and sensitivity
- Diet
- High sugar intake

Assessment of situation

The client had coarse hair on his forehead, above each eyebrow. His skin type was normal/sensitive.

Treatment plan

1 **Easter Vacation:** 30 minutes – two sessions on the same day (one early morning, one last treatment in the afternoon). Each side treated separately for two consecutive weeks.

2 **Summer Vacation:** four months later – treatment as above.

3 **Homecare advice and routine:** specialist electrolysis cream every two hours, for 24 hours after treatment.

The client chose to have his treatment twice a day for two weeks. This suited his active lifestyle. The Blend was used on the 'Sensitive Programme' with a 004 needle. He reacted quite quickly after treatment and the skin was red (the electrolysist found this to be quite usual with the Blend), but the colour soon diffused and there was no further reaction on subsequent days.

Results

As a result of these treatments, the hair was very fine and downy – like 'normal' facial hair. The client was very pleased with the results and decided to have his hair cut short, as he no longer had to attempt to cover up his forehead. The client's change of hairstyle reflected a change of personality. He became more positive, assertive and confident – an instant response to his new look.

CASE HISTORY 3

Avril

*C*lient	Avril – female – of Spanish origin
*A*ge	18
*P*resenting problem	excessive hair growth on chest, abdomen and top lip – referred by doctor

*P*revious history and medical history

The client was referred for electrolysis after extensive endocrine system tests proved negative. The tests showed her still to fall within normal boundaries. The client was very distressed at the extent of her hair problem. There was coarse, terminal, dark hair growth along the collar bone, around the nipples and between the breasts, and from the navel to the pubis. She had 'suffered in silence' from puberty until now, before seeking professional advice and help.

Her school life had been stressful and miserable due to all the sports activities involved in her curriculum. She had encountered endless difficulties trying to keep covered. She appeared very shy and introverted, although academically she was very able and planning to go to university. She had not treated the hair in any way, except for the top lip which she had attempted to bleach.

She had a varied diet and was taking no medication. After consultation she appeared very relieved that, although the treatment would be lengthy and possibly uncomfortable, it would hopefully provide a permanent solution. The client was very quiet and it was difficult to communicate well, but she was obviously highly motivated to carry out a course of treatment.

*P*oints to check

- All relevant points had been medically checked
- Hair growth probably of ethnic origin
- Healing and skin sensitivity
- Diet

*A*ssessment of situation

The client's skin type was oily and she had a pale complexion. The hair growth was coarse, terminal hair, as already indicated in the client history.

*T*reatment plan

All areas were worked on – alternating so that the same area was not being re-treated.

1 Thirty minutes every week for two weeks.
2 Sixty minutes every week for four weeks.
3 Thirty minutes every two weeks for three months.

The treatment began with 30-minute sessions. The client's tolerance level was very good because of her motivation. She was keen to extend the treatment to an hour in order to clear the areas as quickly as possible. Because of the extensive hair growth, it was possible to do this safely without any area being re-treated. After four weeks the therapist resumed 30-minute sessions, to clear regrowth. A 30-minute session once a fortnight was sufficient to keep the area clear.

Throughout these treatments there was considerable variation in current use. The facial hair was removed on quite a low intensity, using a 003 size needle. The body hair required a high intensity current and a longer, 004 size needle. The length of needle was variable.

*R*esults and follow up

Regrowth has been slow and much finer. The client's confidence has improved a great deal. The skin remains in good condition and she is now relaxed and chatting throughout her treatment sessions. It is envisaged that her hair-growth problem could be resolved within the next three months.

Psychologically the effect on her has been enormous. She is about to go on holiday and wear a swimsuit for the first time since childhood and she is looking forward to starting university in October.

This case study shows the dramatic effect that excessive hair growth can have on a young person's life – it demonstrates the positive changes in the client's lifestyle once the threat of regrowth was eliminated.

CASE HISTORY 4

Christine

*C*lient	Christine – female – Caucasian – Scottish
*A*ge	19
*P*resenting problem	unbalanced skin – dry and irritated with occasional eczema and psoriasis; some comedones on chin

*P*revious history and medical history

The client was very distressed about her facial skin which had been unsettled for about two years. The client had a history of eczema and psoriasis on various parts of the body. The client had received, and was still receiving, medical attention. She used a steroid cream when the eczema was severe and a water-based substance for the relief of psoriasis. The client had asked her doctor if she could have beauty treatments, in an attempt to help her facial skin when there was no immediate problem. The doctor approved the beauty treatments.

The client showed sensitivity to most products she had used on the skin. E45, which had been medically suggested, irritated on occasions. The client had been taking an oral contraceptive for six months and, in retrospect, she had noticed a deterioration in her skin in the last four months. The client's monthly cycle was irregular. Her stress level was high due to the concern about her skin. Her diet was unbalanced and her food and fluid intake were irregular. Her sleep pattern was good, with six to seven hours of uninterrupted sleep.

*P*oints to check

- Eczema
- Psoriasis
- Hormones/menstruation
- Oral contraceptive
- Diet (high animal/dairy fat, high sugar)
- Stress level

*A*ssessment of situation

The client's facial skin was free from eczema, but there was evidence of areas that had been affected by this. The eyelids, cheeks and neck had a pink appearance and dryness was apparent. The texture was taut, dry and coarse.

The skin showed extreme sensitivity and, when touched, slight erythema was noticeable. There were small areas of raised pimples in clusters, which were apparent when there was irritation or allergy. The client stated that even water alone made her skin feel irritated. There were a few comedones on the chin area.

*T*reatment plan

| 1 Facial every two weeks for four weeks. |
| 2 Facial every three to four weeks for three months. |
| 3 Facial every month – ongoing. |
| 4 Homecare advice and routine. |

Initially, as the client's skin reacted to touch and products, a light cleansing was completed using a solution of pure, refined soya oil and English bottled water (still). The skin appeared to tolerate this. The cleansing method was repeated and then the skin was treated with pads soaked only in water. A very light massage followed, using the pure refined soya oil which has a fine texture and is able to slide easily over the skin. The client showed signs of erythema, so pressure was modified accordingly. Lymph drainage movements were continued, but applied very lightly. The client experienced no irritation, but was aware of a warmth created by the massage.

The skin was allowed to adjust after the massage and then all traces of oil were removed with damp pads. A French product for diffusing redness and calming sensitive skins was used in a cream mask form. The skin appeared to tolerate this and total absorption produced a calming effect. The client was surprised that the skin had not reacted more violently.

A suggested homecare plan was to use oil and bottled water as a cleanser/lubricator, and to spread a minute portion of oil across the surface of the skin as a protection and to alleviate the dry, taut feeling which the client experienced. It was suggested that the client contact her doctor regarding the oral contraceptive and seek his advice in relation to hormones and her present skin condition. The client was also prepared to look at and alter her present diet.

Two weeks later the client had a second facial. There was some change in the texture of the skin and the irregular patches were less noticeable. The client's doctor had suggested changing her oral contraceptive, but at this stage the client chose to stop taking it altogether.

Over a period of three months, the skin was treated with very few products. When the therapist attempted to introduce another product, the skin reacted quickly and noticeably.

After four months, the same pattern of treatment was used and different nut oils were substituted instead of using creams. The client's skin responded well to pure sweet almond oil and pure refined soya. The existing comedones were removed. The skin showed a more balanced appearance with a more even tone and softer texture. The client had made an attempt to improve her diet by eating a wider variety of food and eating and drinking more regularly. The client's stress level was also reduced because her anxiety about her skin had lessened.

The client went on vacation at this time, to a warmer climate. The skin responded well to the increased sunlight and the psoriasis on the body improved.

Results and follow up

Three years later, the client's skin presents a more stable condition. She is now able to tolerate a mild toner, but not for constant use. The client understands her skin problem more and is aware of the ups and downs which accompany her monthly cycle (i.e. a repeat of earlier patterns of dry red and white patches). Using this limited treatment, there has been a general improvement in the texture and appearance of the skin. The skin is more balanced and less reactive. It responds favourably to massage and positively glows after treatment. The French product for sensitive skins is used regularly and has nutritive qualities. The client has maintained monthly facials and homecare.

The medical practitioner has commented on the improved appearance of the facial skin and has advised the client to continue with treatments.

There are a variety of treatments that could be used with this skin-type, but caution is of paramount importance. Aromatherapy would be the next treatment I would consider. The client's peace of mind is a major issue. She has a natural reluctance to change because of earlier experiences. She has a positive approach to her skin and seeing changes for the better has encouraged her to maintain her present programme. It is interesting to note how quickly the skin can react positively to compatible substances. The client uses only bottled (still) water on her face and this has made a considerable difference to the skin.

20–30

CASE HISTORY 5

May

C*lient*	May – female – Caucasian – English
A*ge*	20 – student
P*resenting problem*	long, dark hair at base of spine

P*revious history and medical history*

The client was referred by her local GP. The doctor explained that the client had mild spina bifida and that there was long, dark hair at the base of her backbone which caused her to be very self-conscious. There were no contra-indications to treatment.

The client had a healthy diet and was generally well. She was a keen sportswoman. No further information was available.

P*oints to check*

- Medical
- Skin healing
- Sugar intake and balanced diet
- Psychological situation

A*ssessment of situation*

The client had terminal hair at the base of the spine. Her skin type was normal.

*T*reatment plan

Every Summer vacation over a three year period:

1 **First year:** 30 minutes every week for eight weeks.
2 **Second year:** 30 minutes every week for six weeks.
3 **Third year:** 30 minutes every week for three weeks.
4 Homecare advice and routine.

*R*esults

The client responded favourably to treatment and after the last treatment the hair was almost completely removed, with just a few downy hairs left. The client was pleased and her self-confidence improved.

It is interesting to note that, although this hair was not visible very often (possibly in a swimsuit), the client suffered as much as someone with a more prominent hair problem.

CASE HISTORY 6

Gary

Client	Gary – male – Caucasian – South African
Age	20
Presenting problem	excess hair growth between eyebrows

Previous history and medical history

The client, a university student, contacted the electrolysist about having the hair removed from between his eyebrows. He was very concerned about the problem because his colleagues and friends said that he always looked cross. The client was young and healthy. No further medical history was available.

Points to check

- Skin healing
- Medical health

Assessment of situation

The client had excess terminal hair between his eyebrows. It was suggested that this should be thinned out rather than totally removed. His skin type was normal/oily.

*T*reatment plan

1 Thirty minutes every month for two years, using moderate current intensity and 003 needle.
2 Homecare advice and routine relating to hygiene of area treated.

The client had the hair thinned out, rather than total removal which would have looked unnatural with his hair growth.

*R*esults

The client attended regularly and the hair growth gradually decreased and was finally cleared. It responded well to epilation. The client was very happy with the result and his confidence increased as a consequence.

The study shows how such an apparently small detail, when corrected, really changed a person's life and may have prevented the development of a psychological problem.

CASE HISTORY 7

Mia

Client   Mia – female – Asian/Indian
Age   20
Presenting problem   excessive hair growth on body, neck and face

Previous history and medical history

The client was very shy and lacked confidence. She had a history of body/ facial hair since puberty and had seen several doctors regarding this problem. She had no monthly periods, a thinning of scalp hair and a receding hairline. She also had a tendency to gain weight, and had an oily skin with slight acne.

She was finally diagnosed as having Stein Leventhal syndrome (polycystic ovaries), but, because of her lack of confidence and lack of parental support, she did not receive the hormone therapy needed. Initially, the doctors had said she needed a hysterectomy, but her parents could not accept this as it would restrict her marriage options (an arranged marriage was anticipated). No further medical treatment was pursued and no alternatives were suggested.

The client was recommended to the teaching establishment where the therapist worked, and she proceeded to have epilation. Until this time she had hoped that the problem would 'just go away'. No further information was available.

Points to check

- Any previous medication, e.g. steroids
- Hormones
- Endocrine system
- Medical approval

- General health
- Psychological situation

*A*ssessment of situation

The client had oily facial skin, with slight acne. There was excessive dense, terminal hair on her face, neck, shoulders, chest, arms and back.

*T*reatment plan

1 Sixty minutes – two to three sessions every week for five years. All areas treated.
2 Sixty minutes every three months and ongoing.

The areas to be treated were very large and therefore considerable treatment time was allowed. The cheeks, chin and neck were treated with short wave diathermy. For the first four years a size 005 needle was used with a moderate current. After this, the therapist was able to change to a 004 needle.

*R*esults and follow-up

The client responded well to treatment, although, as expected, it took a considerable time because of the large areas to be treated and the density of the hair growth.

Throughout the treatment there were obvious changes in the client's personality and appearance. Initially she wore her long sari and veil, and kept her head down so as not to have to speak with people. When the hair growth problem gradually decreased, she became more outgoing. She stopped wearing her veil and generally took more interest in life. Her confidence increased and she appeared a happier person.

The treatment continued for five years and the results were favourable. As the hair growth decreased and became finer, the sessions reduced and so did the frequency of treatment. The client still attends once every three months for an hour's session.

There is no doubt that this treatment has been very advantageous for Mia. This study shows the results that can be achieved with perseverance.

CASE HISTORY 8

Jim

Client   Jim – male – Caucasian –
                            South African
Age   20+
Presenting problem   excess hair on hairline,
                            following hair transplant

Previous history and medical history

The client had had a hair transplant and felt that there was too much hair on the hairline, making his forehead appear narrow. The surgeon who had carried out the transplant suggested that the client should have electrolysis, as surgically he was unable to remove the tufts.

The client attended the therapist's school as a model. The first consultation/ treatment showed the skin to be incredibly tender, so the therapist suggested that he waited until deep healing had taken place. She asked the client to return in three months.

Points to check
- Medical information
- Skin healing and sensitivity

Assessment of situation

After three months, the therapist re-assessed the situation. The skin still looked tender, but there was evidence that subcutaneous healing had taken place. The hair was coarse.

*T*reatment plan

1 Thirty minutes every week for 18 months, with an occasional week being missed because of skin sensitivity.
2 Detailed homecare advice for hygiene and to promote healing.

This client's condition was an unusual and challenging task. The insertion of the needle into the tufts was very difficult. It was also uncomfortable and sometimes painful for the client. The current was therefore very low (with coarse hair a slightly higher current would have been preferred). The treatment was slow and designed to make the client as comfortable as possible. Healing was generally good. Occasionally, when the therapist felt the skin required a longer healing period, she would postpone the treatment. (The client would get very upset as he was very keen to make progress as quickly as possible.)

*R*esults

After 18 months the client was extremely happy with the final result. The hairline was considerably improved.

CASE HISTORY 9

Pete

*C*lient	Pete – male – Caucasian – South African
*A*ge	20+
*P*resenting problem	male model wanted hair removed on upper shoulders

*P*revious history and medical history
None available

*P*oints to check
- Medical health
- Skin healing

*A*ssessment of situation
The client had heavy body hair on his shoulders. His skin type was normal.

*T*reatment plan

> 3 years total
>
> 1 **First year:** 60 minutes, twice a week (different area treated each time).
> 2 **Second year:** 60 minutes, once a week.
> 3 **Third year:** 60 minutes, once a month.
> 4 Homecare advice and routine for hygiene of the areas treated.

The client wanted the hair removed from his upper shoulders because he was a male model. It was a large area to work on and, being body hair, the follicles were shallow. A high current intensity was therefore used with a 003 needle. The client responded favourably but, due to the large area to be treated, this took a considerable time.

*R*esults

This study emphasises the importance that body hair can have for the individual. The final result in this case was a totally clear area, and the client was very satisfied.

CASE HISTORY 10

Frances

*C*lient	Frances – female – Asian
*A*ge	23
*P*resenting problem	pustular and cystic acne – minor scarring

*P*revious history and medical history

The client enjoyed good health. She had suffered with acne since puberty (14 years old) and also had very greasy hair. She had an irregular menstrual cycle. Doctors were not concerned about the menstruation, but treated her skin condition with antibiotics and lotions which peeled the client's skin. The client had not responded to treatment over a four-year period – there would be a slight improvement, then the skin would regress. The client felt that her skin benefited from sunshine after a long period (i.e. four weeks).

The client's diet was vegetarian with a high curry and cereal intake. It contained little protein and few vegetables. Chocolate was eaten three to four times each week. The fluid intake was also low – mainly water, with some fruit juice and occasional coffee.

The client slept well – seven to eight hours. She was generally relaxed, but felt that her skin condition created stress. Sometimes she would try to cover her face with her hair, which aggravated the problem. She had a regular cleansing routine, but was always changing products.

*P*oints to check

- Diet
- Menstrual problems
- Stress level
- Endocrine system

*A*ssessment of situation

The skin appeared oily and there were open pores around the nose, cheeks and chin. There was evidence of pustules in clusters and of comedones. The skin texture was uneven. There was evidence of inflammation in patches around the face. The scalp was very oily.

*T*reatment plan

```
1  Facial every six weeks for six years – ongoing.
2  Homecare advice and routine.
```

It was only possible, due to the client's financial situation, to see her every six weeks. An initial facial included comedone extraction and biological exfoliation. A lavender-based massage cream and a mild camphor range of products were used. After the facial, the skin appeared less inflamed, less oily and brighter.

The client was given detailed homecare advice, using the indicated camphor products which she chose to purchase. She was asked to keep a daily record of her diet and skin appearance, and to note her monthly menstrual pattern. She was advised to reduce her chocolate intake (there are two schools of thought regarding chocolate, but this therapist found, from experience, that chocolate does aggravate some skin problems) and a greater fluid intake was recommended.

Over a period of six months, the client noticed that there was a change in the secretion of oil on the skin. The skin appeared brighter and there was some reduction in scar tissue. The 'record book' was checked regularly and adjustments were considered to balance the daily diet. The client eventually eliminated chocolate from her diet completely and she noticed that the characteristics of the pustules were different – the red/purple inflammation subsided and the 'angry' appearance was reduced. The occasional cyst still developed, mainly in the cheek area, but these were reduced.

After one year, a pattern was developing which showed the skin to be reactive during the client's menstruation – the cycle varied from three to ten weeks. The client's very irregular menstrual cycle was clearly a major contributory factor, but, as the client did not want to take hormone preparations, the doctor felt he could provide no other assistance. The client was also aware that heavily spiced foods caused a skin reaction.

After two years, the client's treatments included aromatherapy, some Direct High Frequency and continued use of biological exfoliation masks. She also wore medicated cover make-up, which gave her more confidence as she was not so aware of her skin condition. The client felt that she was more in control of the situation because the skin erupted less frequently. Her skin texture had improved and the appearance was brighter. She followed a good cleansing routine and regular six-weekly facials maintained the skin. The scar tissue was considerably reduced and there was no evidence of vitiligo, which often accompanies this skin type.

Results and follow-up

After six years, the client no longer suffers with acne, but sebaceous glands still react violently on occasions and one or two spots tend to appear pre-menstrually. The client favours homoeopathic medicine and she is still seeking assistance with her gynaecological problem, but as yet this has not been forthcoming. Her skin appears bright, soft and healthy.

This study demonstrates that the client has learned to control her skin problem and to come to terms with her menstrual problem. She has also been able to adopt a more positive attitude towards other problems.

———

Aromatherapy is a **specialist treatment** *– see page 127 for further details.*

CASE HISTORY I I

Vicky

***C**lient*	Vicky – female – Asian
***A**ge*	23
***P**resenting problem*	excessive hair growth on upper lips, sides of face, jawline and upper neck

Previous history and medical history

The client came to the electrolysist by recommendation. She was very distressed by scabs and skin infection which had arisen since treatment with her previous electrolysist. The condition could have resulted from poor hygiene, inadequate homecare advice or inaccurate insertions at too high a current.

The client had first noticed superfluous hair growth at puberty (quite common with this ethnic group), but did not attempt to have it removed. Two years ago the client had decided she no longer wanted the excess hair and therefore had wax treatments regularly for twelve months. She had then tried electrolysis for six months in an attempt to find a more permanent solution, but suffered from scabs and infection. Her problem was actually being added to rather than reduced. She was obviously stressed about this experience and was very reluctant to attempt further treatment. She was very self-conscious and wore her hair around her face to hide the hair growth.

The client's general health was good with no medical problems, serious illnesses or recent operations. She had a regular monthly cycle. She was a moderate smoker.

Points to check

- Endocrine system
- Stress
- Skin healing and sensitivity
- Any previous medication, e.g. steroids

Assessment of situation

The client had an oily skin which usually healed quickly. There was excessive terminal hair on the upper lips, sides of face, jawline and upper neck. There was evidence that infection had been present and one or two small scabs.

Treatment plan

1. One 15-minute treatment each side of face, using 004 needle and low current.
2. Homecare – to bathe area with cooled boiled water.
3. Two days later – skin assessed for reaction.
   One 30-minute treatment in different areas.
4. One week later – full skin-care routine given, including preparation for electrolysis.
   One 45-minute treatment spread over *all* areas.
5. One 45–60 minute treatment approximately every six days for three months, treating all areas.

The therapist commenced treatment cautiously, to see how the client's skin reacted. There appeared to be very little reaction using a 004 needle on a low current. The client was advised of the importance of homecare and was asked to bathe her skin with boiled water that had cooled.

Two days later, the client returned for a skin assessment. There was a favourable response and evidence that the skin healed quickly. The client was keen to have further hairs removed, so different areas were treated for 30 minutes.

One week later, the client was given a cleanse, tone and moisturise homecare routine. She was also advised to use a salt paste the day before treatment, to prepare the skin further for electrolysis. The client's skin was oily and thick in texture. This mild exfoliation assisted the treatment and ensured a good skin condition. The client also had a 45-minute treatment spread over several areas. The skin response was good and the client was pleased and eager to continue the treatment. She then received treatment every six days for 45–60 minutes, spreading the treatment over all the areas.

*R*esults and follow-up

After three months, 003 needles were used for regrowth, which was considerably less and much finer. The client was then confident enough to change her hairstyle and to tie it back from her face. She smiled more and showed an improved posture, holding her head high and her shoulders back. The client tended to trim any hair regrowth between treatments, but when she went on holiday she had her hair cut short and felt comfortable enough not to use any method of hair removal until her return.

The treatment is still progressing well, with no adverse skin reactions, excellent healing, much finer, lighter regrowth – and a confident, happy, client.

CASE HISTORY 12

Melanie

***C**lient*	Melanie – female – Caucasian – American
***A**ge*	25
***P**resenting problem*	unbalanced skin – some spots/ red rashes

Previous history and medical history

The client had been experiencing problems with her skin for about seven months. The skin never appeared settled and was becoming increasingly sensitive. Her cleansing routine had become spasmodic because of irritation. The client had been taking oral contraceptives for two years. Her diet used to be balanced and varied, but in the last year she had been increasingly eating snack foods. She had a low fluid intake (no water was included) and a high intake of animal fats, with very few vegetables and fruit. The client's previous skin-care products had been satisfactory until the skin started to irritate. The client enjoyed good general health and was taking no medication. She had had no recent operations.

Points to check

- Diet (unbalanced, high sugar/high fat intake)
- Hormones
- Menstruation
- Oral contraceptive
- Products used on the skin

*A*ssessment of situation

The client had dry, sensitive skin with an oily nose area and irritated rashes along the sides of the cheeks. Her skin texture was uneven, with white, dry areas and irregular colour.

*T*reatment plan

1 First facial.
2 Second facial, two weeks later.
3 Third facial, two weeks later.
4 Monthly maintenance facial.
5 Homecare advice and routine.

Initially the client's skin responded well to a mild cleanser and toner. Although the skin was easily stimulated by touch, a half-strength solution of lavender oil was used to give the skin a light massage. This improved the texture and produced a more even colour. A 'calming' mask (German product) was used to conclude treatment, followed by moisturisation. The client's skin showed an allergic irritation in the dry places, which could have been due to a product in direct contact or a reaction to handling and massaging the skin. However, the skin settled after ten minutes and the colour remained even. The client was given homecare advice and, in addition to cleansing and toning (using products at half-strength), it was suggested she should attempt to vary her diet, increase her vegetable/fruit intake and drink some water. The client continued to use a half-strength solution of lavender oil between treatments, three to four times a week, for light massage.

The second treatment was two weeks later. The skin had improved and the red rashes had started to subside. The client had also made a good attempt to improve her diet. Treatment followed a similar pattern. By the third treatment, two weeks later, the skin showed no signs of allergic reaction. The texture was smooth, the colour was even and the skin was balanced.

*R*esults and follow-up

The client felt that the skin-care treatment assisted the problem which was obviously being caused by her diet. She continues to receive regular monthly facials and has maintained her balanced diet. Her skin is now glowing, healthy and bright, with good tone, colour and elasticity. It is interesting to note how long the skin took to react to its inadequate diet, and how quickly it responded when the intake of vegetables and fruit was increased.

———

Aromatherapy is a **specialist treatment** *– see page 127 for further details.*

CASE HISTORY 13

Susan

Client   Susan – female – Black – African
Age   27
Presenting problem   severe hyperpigmentation

Previous history and medical history

The client had severe hyperpigmentation from using commercial bleaching creams and then over-exposing her face to the sun. She went to various doctors who prescribed stronger concentrates of bleaching creams and advised her to use sunblock. No further client information was available.

Points to check

- General health
- Skin healing and sensitivity
- Hormones

Assessment of situation

The client had severe hyperpigmentation, with considerable evidence of redundant cuticle.

Treatment plan

> 1 Five enzyme treatments.
> 2 Melanoplex System treatment.
> 3 Alpha-hydroxy acid treatment.
> 4 Homecare plan – a daily cleansing routine, and application of 'creme citrique', transdermal sunblock FACTOR 30 and herbal, dark-pigment oil.

Initially, the client had five enzyme treatments to remove the excess redundant cuticle. This was followed by the Melanoplex System to improve the hyperpigmentation. There was a 30% improvement at this stage. The client then elected to have the deeper alpha-hydroxy acid treatment, which resulted in a 75% improvement. The homecare maintenance programme included daily cleansing using a low pH cleanser, and application of 'creme citrique' – a transdermal protein cream which is very acid, containing fermented orange-peel extract and vitamin C. The client was also asked to always use transdermal sunblock when outdoors and to use herbal dark-pigment oil on dark skin areas.

*R*esults

The results were very encouraging and the client was satisfied with her treatment and overall appearance. However, she never re-booked for her maintenance treatment and did not continue with her homecare maintenance programme. She felt that she was 'cured' and that she could revert to her favourite cosmetics and her previous ways. Unfortunately, the problem will resurrect itself again as homecare maintenance is vital after such an intensive treatment programme.

This study shows how quickly the client accepted positive changes without considering the long-term situation and need for maintenance of her improved skin.

———

This is a **specialist treatment** *area – refer to page 122 (hydrolyzation treatment) for more details.*

31–40

CASE HISTORY 14

Marisa

***C**lient*   Marisa – female – Italian

***A**ge*   30+

***P**resenting problem*   excessive black hair on chin
and neck, some hair on upper
lip (later revealed hair on
body)

Previous history and medical history

A student at the therapist's school asked the client to come as a model. She
was extremely shy and nervous about coming for treatment. She appeared
very withdrawn and embarrassed about her hair growth. Her parents had
not allowed her to have any treatment when she was younger and she had
resorted to bleaching the hair. The client's condition had caused her
psychological problems as described above.

The client had good general health with no serious illnesses or recent
operations. The hair growth appeared at puberty. Italians often classify this
amount of hair growth as normal. No further medical history was available.

Points to check

- Endocrine system
- Skin healing/sensitivity
- Hormones
- Ethnic
- Previous medication, e.g. steroids

Assessment of situation

The client had black hair on her face, upper lip, chin and neck. Her skin type was oily.

Treatment plan

1 Forty-five minutes – three sessions every week for three years (the same area was not re-treated). 005 needle used with moderate current.
2 Homecare advice related to hygiene of the area treated.

Results and follow-up

The hair growth was dense and the chin and upper neck were the main areas of priority initially. The client responded well to treatment and healed quickly. Her psychological situation improved and she became happier and more outgoing. She joined a dance group – something she had never considered previously.

Once the chin and neck had responded well, the therapist proceeded to treat the other areas. Finally, the client revealed that she also had considerable hair growth on her chest and that she wanted this treated. The results were good and the hair growth cleared.

This study shows the importance of developing the client's confidence prior to and during treatment. The therapist's care and understanding were vital considerations in the initial stages of treatment. It is sad to note how long this client had suffered with her hair-growth problem, throughout the prime years of her life.

CASE HISTORY 15

Tim
———

*C*lient   Tim – male – Caucasian –
                                 English
*A*ge   33
*P*resenting problem   long hair all over body

*P*revious history and medical history

The client was referred to the therapist by his local doctor. He was very self-conscious about his body hair, which grew very thick and long, about four inches in length, and appeared like an animal pelt. He had become too embarrassed to reveal his upper body and would not go on holiday.

The client was unable to supply detailed medical information, but he appeared to have generally good health. He had vague memories of being treated in a London hospital when he was four years old, because his growth was stunted. He thought that he had been given hormone treatment. This could have affected his hair growth. He was still very short in stature.

Two years ago he had been in a serious motor cycle accident which resulted in metal pins in his legs. As the treatment was not on the legs it was not medically contra-indicated.

*P*oints to check

- Endocrine system
- Medical detail
- Skin healing and sensitivity
- Previous medication, e.g. steroids

*A*ssessment of situation

The client had excessive hair growth all over the body.

*T*reatment plan

Areas treated: upper and lower arms, back of neck, upper back and upper chest.

1 Sixty minutes – two sessions every week for 32 weeks.
2 Thirty minutes – two sessions every week for 16 weeks and continuing.
3 Aftercare/homecare – specialist electrolysis cream every two hours, for 24 hours after treatment.

The Blend was used on the Programme for Coarse Hair – needle size 004 and 005. There was some immediate erythema, but then the skin was calm. The response was good and the client was so pleased that he wanted a lot of small areas treated. The client was advised of the importance of aftercare throughout the treatment.

*R*esults and follow-up

Treatment is still continuing. So far the hair has gone completely from the upper arms and has thinned out on the lower arms. The upper chest around the clavicle is clear, as are the neck and top area of the upper back. The client is more self-assured and, as his confidence in the treatment has developed, he is beginning to see a 'permanent' solution to this problem.

The case highlights the importance of the rapport between client and therapist in achieving beneficial results, both physically and mentally. The therapist felt that good verbal communication was particularly important with this client.

CASE HISTORY 16

Jane

Client	Jane – female – Caucasian – Australian (lives in South Australia)
Age	34
Presenting problem	acne on upper back

Previous history and medical history

The client had suffered with pustular acne on the upper back for several years. She was very self-conscious about the condition and kept the area covered. It had never been exposed to sunlight.

The client was healthy. There was no history of serious illnesses and she had not had any operations. She occasionally suffered from constipation.

She had a well-balanced diet with a low alcohol consumption. However, her fluid intake was low and she drank very little water. She was a non-smoker and took regular exercise, walking two miles daily with her dog. Her menstrual cycle was regular and she had no hormone problems. The client was concerned about her back, so there was some evidence of stress.

Points to check

- Hormones
- Endocrine system
- Stress

Assessment of situation

The client had pustulated spots on the upper back. Her skin was red and inflamed, but this was in specific areas rather than all over the upper back. The skin type was coarse and oily.

Treatment plan

1 Direct High Frequency and aromatherapy back massage using lavender oil.
2 Homecare routine – daily lavender baths.
3 Seven days later – Direct High Frequency, clay mask and aromatherapy back massage/lavender oil.
4 Four days later – Direct High Frequency with lavender oil and aromatherapy massage.
5 Sixty-second exposure to midday sun for the area treated, increasing to 90 seconds (10 second increase per day).
6 Five days later – Direct High Frequency with lavender oil and aromatherapy massage.

Initially the therapist used Direct High Frequency on the client's skin with talcum powder, employing the 'sparking method'. This was followed by massaging the area with a little neat lavender essential oil. (Lavender is one of the few essential oils that can be applied in small quantities without being mixed with a carrier oil.) There was an immediate response – the redness was reduced, diffusing quickly after the Direct High Frequency and even more so after the lavender oil. The client was asked to follow a simple homecare routine – to have a daily bath using a few drops of lavender essential oil to soothe the skin and to ensure relaxation.

Seven days later the second treatment consisted of Direct High Frequency as before. A clay mask was also used to extract impurities in the skin and the client was then massaged with a little neat lavender essential oil. The client had increased her daily water intake.

The third treatment, four days later, followed the same pattern as the initial treatment. The skin was beginning to maintain a more favourable response. The pustules had cleared and the redness was very slight, diffusing well after treatment. After this treatment, the client was advised for homecare to expose the treated area to the midday sun for 60 seconds, and to increase this by 10 seconds a day up to a maximum of 90 seconds.

The fourth treatment, five days later, showed that the condition had cleared up. The client, however, chose to continue to have weekly back massage and to occasionally use lavender baths.

*R*esults and follow-up

The client was generally relaxed and pleased with the results. Her skin maintained its healthier appearance, but she continued to enjoy a weekly back massage for well-being.

The client was also shown a light abdominal massage to use when she became constipated. However, this was not really necessary as, once the client had increased her water intake quite considerably, the problem no longer occurred.

This study shows how treatment of the whole person helped this client with other problems, as well as the presenting skin condition.

――――

Aromatherapy is a **specialist treatment** *– see page 127 for further details.*

CASE HISTORY 17

Simon

Client   Simon – male – Spanish
Age   34
Presenting problem   heavy eyebrow growth

Previous history and medical history

The client had been aware of heavy eyebrow growth since the age of fourteen – this is often associated with his ethnic group. His eyebrows were very heavy and met in the middle. This gave the client a rather unpleasant facial expression, which caused him some psychological concern. The client worked in the retail trade for a large beauty company and he felt that removal of the hair between his eyebrows would make him more visually pleasing to his associates and the public.

The client's general health was good and, apart from pneumonia at ten years of age, he had experienced no medical problems and was taking no medication. He led an active working life and had a busy lifestyle.

Points to check
- Genetics
- Previous medication, e.g. steroids
- Skin healing and sensitivity

Assessment of situation
The client had heavy eyebrow growth, as previously stated. He had no skin problems.

*T*reatment plan

Four treatments over two months:

1 twenty minutes – including consultation;
2 twenty minutes;
3 fifteen minutes;
4 ten minutes.

The first treatment was for 20 minutes, including the consultation. The client was comfortable with the current, and the intensity was moderate. The response was good and a large amount of brow was treated. One week later the same pattern of treatment was given and more brow was cleared. The skin responded well. The third treatment was given two weeks later. This time the treatment duration was fifteen minutes. The current intensity was the same as previously and all the necessary hair was removed from the particular area being treated. The skin responded well. The fourth and final treatment was two weeks later. The treatment duration was ten minutes and the current intensity was the same. All new growth was cleared.

*R*esults and follow-up

The client was very satisfied with the result. He was pleased with his new look and gained a considerable increase in confidence. He felt it would benefit his career progression as well as his personal life.

The client was advised to return if regrowth occurred, but to date this has not been necessary.

CASE HISTORY 18

Jo

Client   Jo – male – Chinese
Age   34
Presenting problem   severe acne rosacea

Previous history and medical history

The client had suffered from severe acne for many years. He had undergone intensive treatments from several dermatologists – they had all used antibiotics and topical anti-inflammatory salves, but to no avail. No further client details were available.

Points to check

- Hormones
- Endocrine system
- Diet
- Skin healing and sensitivity

Assessment of situation

The client had severe acne rosacea with dead cell build-up.

Treatment plan

1 Three enzyme treatments.
2 Alpha-hydroxy acid 'peel'.
3 Daily homecare – cleansing routine.
4 Enzyme treatments at the clinic – bi-monthly.
5 Twice weekly homecare – enzyme mask treatments.
6 Daily use of sunblock FACTOR 30 (containing no oil).

The client's treatment commenced with three enzyme treatments to hydrolyse all the dead cell build-up. This cleared the rosacea crusts and lowered the inflammation caused by this redundant cuticle layer. The client then received an alpha-hydroxy acid 'peel' – a one day procedure followed by six days of 'wallpaper coming off' effect. The result was a 75% overall improvement.

The homecare programme following this consisted of a daily cleansing routine with a low pH herbal cleanser (natural surfactants) compounded from Ritha plant extract, yucca plant and oak bark.

The client then received bi-monthly enzyme treatments at the clinic. 'Acu creme', a transdermal, water soluble protein cream with plant enzymes and vitamin C, was applied. This substance moistens the skin without adding extra oil. Twice weekly the client also performs his own enzyme mask treatment, which is a modified version of the professional treatment that he received at the clinic.

It is necessary for the client to use a sunblock when going out of doors, to prevent post-peel hyperpigmentation which is very common in oriental skins. He applies transdermal sunblock FACTOR 30, which does not contain oil.

*R*esults

This study shows how quickly the client's skin improved, in comparison with the years that he had suffered from the condition.

———

This is a **specialist treatment** *– refer to page 122 (hydrolyzation treatment) for more details.*

CASE HISTORY 19

Christie

Client	Christie – female – Caucasian – Canadian
Age	39
Presenting problem	fine dark hair on upper lip

Previous history and medical history

The client's medical history was very good. She was a model and therefore maintained a healthy, youthful body, kept to a strict balanced diet and took regular daily exercise. The client had experienced chloasma in two earlier pregnancies. She was taking no medication.

Points to check

- Hormones
- Skin healing and sensitivity
- Chloasma
- Vitiligo

Assessment of situation

The client had very fine, dark hair on her upper lip, which she wanted removed. The growth area was slight and this type of growth is commonly seen. The client's skin type was normal and was in excellent condition.

*T*reatment plan

> 1 Fifteen minutes every two weeks for two months. No treatment during pregnancy because of a tendency to chloasma.
> 2 Treatment resumed one year later – 15 minutes every two weeks for three months.

The treatment commenced with 15-minute sessions, once a fortnight for two months. The client then informed the therapist that she was pregnant. As she had suffered from chloasma in previous pregnancies, it was thought advisable to discontinue treatment until after the pregnancy. The hair was bleached in the meantime. Treatment recommenced six months after the birth.

*R*esults

After a further three months of treatment as before, the hair growth was permanently cleared. It is interesting to note that there was no change in the growth during pregnancy.

This study demonstrates how a relatively normal hair growth can respond to treatment.

CASE HISTORY 20

Louise

Client   Louise – female – Caucasian –
                        English

Age   40

Presenting problem poor, dry and dehydrated
                        ageing skin

Previous history and medical history

The client's skin was in poor condition and showed sun-damage. She had used sunbeds excessively since she was thirty years old. She maintained a healthy diet, had no apparent medical problems and was not taking any medication. The client was, however, very stressed. She had recently divorced.

Points to check

- Health
- Hormones
- Stress
- Environment/sun
- Balanced diet
- Fluid intake

Assessment of situation

The client had poor, dehydrated skin due to sun damage.

Microscopic analysis

The microscopic skin test revealed that the connective tissue fibres had been repeatedly exposed to solar radiation. The fibres that were present were not very strong. The skin showed evidence that regeneration had taken place several times. This was indicated by the collagenic and elastinic disposition of the skin.

Treatment plan

1 Microscopic skin analysis test.
2 Monthly facial consisting of a deep cleanse normalisation programme, hand facial massage, and moisturisation.
3 Homecare routine – cleanse and tone twice daily using specialised products; follow normalisation programme for three months.
4 Three months later – microscopic re-test.
5 Monthly maintenance facial.

The client had a monthly facial consisting of a deep cleanse normalisation programme of a gel mask and cream, followed by a hand facial massage and then moisturisation. She was given a homecare routine, which consisted of cleansing and toning twice daily with substances containing water soluble essential oils used to relax the skin tissues.

She also followed the 'normalisation programme', which meant that she used a gel mask twice weekly (containing extracts from the sea which drew water from the dermis to the epidermis by osmosis) and used a nightly normalisation cream to support the treatment. During the day she used an Elastin day cream. This programme lasted for three months and then she continued to use a nightly collagen cream and to follow her daily cleansing, toning and moisturising routine.

Results and follow-up

Microscopic re-test took place after three months. This showed that the connective tissue had improved after the normalisation programme. The client continued to have a monthly facial for skin maintenance.

This microscopic, diagnostic analysis of the skin allows the therapist to 'see' the immediate problem and to be able to give an intensive treatment programme using substances that the skin requires at the time of assessment.

———

This is a **specialist treatment** *– refer to page 126 (microscopic analysis) for further details.*

41–50

CASE HISTORY 21

Mary

Client	Mary – female – Black – African
Age	40+
Presenting problem	excessive curly hair in chin and jaw area

Previous history and medical history

The client had a history of hormone imbalance for over ten years. She was receiving medical treatment for this, but the hair problem had not improved. She was generally healthy and had no other medical problems.

Points to check

- Endocrine system
- Hormones
- Ethnic – skin healing (this skin type is prone to keloid scarring)

Assessment of situation

The client had oily, thickened skin with excessive coarse, curly hair in the jaw area. (The hair type is normal for this ethnic group.)

Treatment plan

1 Thirty minutes every week for 18 months.
2 Thirty minutes every month, using medium current intensity – ongoing.
3 Homecare advice and routine for hygiene of area and skincare.

*R*esults

The client responded well to treatment with no adverse reactions, although the curly hair was extremely difficult to work on because it was very coarse and curly. It was slow to respond, but finally the required result was achieved.

This study provides an interesting contrast to case history 22: Ellie.

CASE HISTORY 22

Ellie

Client   Ellie – female – Black – African
Age   40–50
Presenting problem   patches of coarse hair on chin

Previous history and medical history

The client was very large with a dominant personality. She was menopausal and the hair growth appeared to be associated with this. She was strong and healthy and had had no serious illnesses or recent operations.

Points to check

- Skin healing
- Menopause
- Endocrine system

Assessment of situation

The client had coarse, oily skin, typical of this ethnic group. It was very dark, with some small areas of darker pigmentation. The skin appeared to heal well. This is important because of the tendency to keloid scarring with this skin type. There was curly, coarse, terminal hair in isolated areas on the chin.

*T*reatment plan

> The client was aware of the importance of regular treatments, but chose to attend when she wanted to. This meant long intervals between treatment and a very irregular pattern.
>
> 1 Thirty minutes every three or four months over 18 months. Shortwave diathermy – needle size 004–005, moderate to strong current.
> 2 Homecare advice and routine using specialist cream for electrolysis.

The client's treatment followed no particular pattern. However, the client was asked to note her skin's reactions after treatment. This was monitored carefully, particularly after the first treatment, because of the tendency this skin has to keloid scarring. The treatment went well and there were no adverse reactions. The client was also advised of a homecare routine using a specialist cream for electrolysis that was applied every two hours for 24 hours. Healing was good.

*R*esults

The hair growth was springy and curly and the roots were curly. They responded well and regrowth was finer. The entire treatment period would probably have been shorter if treatments had been closer together.

This study shows that treatment can be successful even if it is not always carried out as the therapist anticipates. However, it would have been difficult to achieve a successful outcome if the hair growth had been more prolific and required more regular treatments.

CASE HISTORY 23

Denise

Client   Denise – female – Caucasian –
                                    English
Age   42
Presenting problem   dry skin, unable to maintain
                                    satisfactory moisture level

Previous history and medical history

The client had a history of hormonal disturbance since her early twenties.
This resulted in a total hysterectomy at 32. Hormones were given as
implants and/or pills. The client suffered with water retention and at the
time of her first appointment she had changed to using HRT patches.

The client's general health was variable. She suffered frequent colds and
some depression caused by the hormone imbalance. The client's sleep
pattern was erratic (also related to the hormone imbalance), but her diet
was varied and she had a good eating pattern. She also took regular exercise.
The client had a regular cleansing routine and used a night cream.

Points to check
- Hormone balance
- Skin sensitivity
- Stress
- Diet

Assessment of situation

The client's skin was dry but not irritated. There was some sign of
photosensitivity. The client used a high factor protection on her face when

sunbathing. The skin appeared dull and listless with a slightly coarse texture. There were some broken capillaries and fine lines.

*T*reatment plan

> 1 Three facials over a four week period.
> 2 Homecare routine.
> 3 Monthly maintenance facial for three months.
> 4 Three facials over a two week period after holiday.

The client's skin was given a facial and a biological 'peel'. The skin responded well, showing no sensitivity to the product. Circulation was improved and a slight erythema became apparent. Aromatherapy creams containing rose oil were used (rose is known for its qualities in balancing the female reproductive system). A cream mask was also used to diffuse capillary action and increase circulation. The product has deep penetration. There was an immediate reaction to the facial – in particular, a softening of the skin. A homecare routine was advised using the aromatherapy cream.

Two further facials were given over a four week period. The skin appeared more stable and a controlled balance was maintained. The client used the cream mask three times a week at home. She felt calmer in herself and pleased with her skin.

Following this the client needed only a monthly maintenance facial. The client's skin progressed well for three months, but was interrupted when the client went on vacation to a very hot climate. At this time the client's hormone patch was changed to a stronger dosage.

The therapist advised the client to be cautious in the sun because of her tendency to photosensitivity on the face and because she was taking HRT. The client's body generally tanned well, but on her return she had several very large patches of vitiligo on her back. She was very perturbed about this. After medical consultation she accepted that the condition was irreversible and was caused by the HRT.

Her face was fortunately not affected. She had used factor 15 throughout the vacation, but the facial skin was dry, probably due to the sun. It responded well to three facials over a two week period.

*R*esults and follow-up

The client's skin maintained its good texture with regular treatment, but vitiligo continued to occur over the body. (The facial skin has not been affected.) A medical specialist tried to reduce the dosage of hormones in order to assist the problem. The situation is still being investigated medically.

There is no doubt that hormones are very important in the maintenance of the skin. This example shows, however, that they can also create quite severe problems. A full understanding of Hormone Replacement Therapy is necessary for the individual's psychological as well as physical well-being.

CASE HISTORY 24

Emma

Client

Age

Presenting problem

Emma – female – Caucasian –
English

44

excessive hair growth on face
and legs

Previous history and medical history

This client had a history of excessive hair growth from the age of 15 and had
undergone intermittent treatment since then. The condition appeared to be
hereditary as her mother had also experienced the same problem since
puberty. (Her mother had been treated with extensive electrolysis over
many years and now had only a few hairs in regrowth.)

The client's lifestyle was very busy. Her job was very demanding but she
enjoyed this. She made time to socialise and enjoyed the Arts in particular.
She appeared to be a very intense person. She followed a balanced diet,
eating three meals a day, and she took regular exercise in the form of dance
classes.

The client wanted total removal of the hair. She had experienced long
sessions previously with other electrolysists and wanted to follow the same
pattern this time. The client's health was good and she had a good healing
record. She was taking no medication.

Points to check
- Hereditary
- Sensitivity
- Menstrual cycle and pattern of hair growth

- Stress
- Endocrine system.

*A*ssessment of situation

The client's skin type was sensitive, with dilated capillaries on the face and dry, pale skin. There was excessive hair growth on her face, brow and upper lip, and thick, dark hair over the entire leg area.

*T*reatment plan

1 Sixty minutes every week for six months (alternate areas).
2 Three-month break.
3 Sixty minutes every two weeks for nine months (alternate areas).
4 Three-month break.
5 Thirty minutes every two weeks for nine months.

The client first came here for electrolysis treatment three years ago. She had been used to having one hour's treatment from other electrolysists. The present therapist was reluctant to treat a single area for this time, but explained that she could alternate the areas. The client accepted this. The therapist explained that treatment was dependent on healing.

For six months the client had weekly treatment on different areas. The healing pattern was good. The client then chose to stop for three months during the summer, as she wanted to go bare-legged but not sunbathe. Treatment recommenced after this time for a further nine months.

The treatment time was adjusted to suit the client's sensitivity, as it became apparent that the thighs and just below the buttock were delicate areas. These areas also took longer to heal. Her tolerance level varied and there was increased sensitivity prior to menstruation or if the client was stressed. On these occasions the therapist epilated very few hairs because low tolerance coincided with poor healing.

After the nine months the client took a three-month summer break, as before, and then treatment recommenced for a further nine months. The treatment time was adjusted to 30 minutes every two weeks. The break in treatment was good because it became clear that regrowth was slower and that the problem was gradually being solved. There was less hair on the client's face, but treatment was cautious due to her sensitive skin. The facial skin responded well and there was no extreme sensitivity as had been evidenced on the thighs. The intensity of the current was much lower on the face.

*R*esults and follow-up

At present the client is taking her summer break from electrolysis. The therapist anticipates that there will be some regrowth in the knee area during this time, which will be treated in the autumn. The hairs on the knees have been very strong and slowest to respond. A higher current has been necessary for this area.

The client will be advised to have treatment two or three times per year, in order to clear any regrowth.

It should be noted in this case study that low tolerance of the current intensity coincided with slower healing. It is vital to always be aware of the individual's response during treatment – the body's reaction is a good indicator of how treatment should continue.

CASE HISTORY 25

June

Client
June – female – Caucasian – English

Age
47

Presenting problem
small area of strong hairs on chin

Previous history and medical history

The client had good health generally, but a recent scan had shown evidence of osteoporosis. The client was taking Hormone Replacement Therapy for this. No further information was available.

Points to check

- HRT
- Endocrine system

Assessment of situation

The client had an oily skin, which healed well but was prone to blemishes. She had 12 terminal hairs on the chin.

Treatment plan

10 minutes – blend.

The client had 10 minutes of epilation to remove the 12 terminal hairs from her chin. A 003 needle was used and the current intensity was moderate.

*R*esults

The client's skin did react quite noticeably after treatment -- it became red but there was no discomfort. Regrowth was very slight and the hairs that did regrow simply fell out! This was an unusual situation that the therapist had not previously experienced. The client was pleased with the result.

CASE HISTORY 26

Helen

Client   Helen – female – Caucasian –
                                    English
Age   49
Presenting problem   oily, lumpy, acne-scarred skin
                                    with open pores

Previous history and medical history

The client had suffered with acne vulgaris as a teenager and well into her
twenties. She had always cleansed the skin, but did not know how to treat
the problem. Medical advice to 'leave it alone' had been given in the early
stages.

After seven years, the acne did subside but the scars remained. These had
become more noticeable as the skin matured. The client had always wanted
to do something about her skin and the scars, but she was uncertain what
was available and did not wish to have operations or harsh treatment.

The client's health was good, although recently she had been aware of
menopausal symptoms – irregular cycle. She noted that her skin appeared
more oily at this time. The client had a good cleansing routine. She did not
usually wear make-up as it tended to disappear quickly due to the oiliness of
her skin. Various brands had been tried but they all reacted in the same way.

The client had a varied diet, enjoying fruit and raw vegetables as snacks. She
drank regular fluids, including water, and had a low sugar intake. The client
was, however, about eight kilograms overweight. She slept well and
maintained a seven hour sleep pattern. She was taking no medication and
there was no history of allergies.

Points to check

- Endocrine system
- Hormones
- Menopause
- Skin sensitivity

Assessment of situation

The client's skin appeared firm with enlarged pores. The colour was uneven – sallow and red around the chin. It was oily and there was evidence of oedema around the eyes and cheeks. There was also evidence of heavy scar tissue over the entire face, and the skin appeared pitted. The benefits of chemical and biological peeling were discussed with the client. She preferred the milder form of biological exfoliation and a treatment programme was costed and explained. The client decided to have a course of treatment.

Treatment plan

1. Biological peel every week for six weeks.
2. Facial massage with nutritive plant extracts – 20 minutes every week for six weeks.
3. Homecare – cleansing, toning and moisturising; daily nutritive plant extract masks.
4. Biological peel every three weeks (scarred area) for six months.
5. Biological peel every four weeks (entire face) for six months.
6. Maintenance facial every month with biological peel.

Initially, the skin was cleansed deeply and a biological peel was carried out. There was a very slight change in the texture of the skin after this. A 20-minute facial massage then followed. The skin responded well to massage, in particular to petrissage movements and lymphatic drainage. The firm, mask-like appearance of the facial skin softened slightly and the face shape, texture and colour improved. The client was pleased with the change in her skin, which appeared brighter overall and less oily.

The entire facial, including peeling, was repeated for six weeks (according to the manufacturer's instructions on biological peeling). The client was also encouraged to use nutritive plant extract masks daily at home in order to revitalise the skin. After four weeks there was a definite improvement in the skin – old scar tissue was less and the texture was smoother. The oiliness was reduced and the colour was more even. After six weeks there were further positive changes and the skin looked more balanced and healthy. The scar tissue had been reduced.

The treatment pattern then changed to biological peeling for the scarred areas every three weeks and for the entire face every four weeks. This pattern continued for six months.

*R*esults and follow-up

By the end of the six months, significant improvement was apparent. The client's skin was smoother, scarred lumps were reduced and a healthier skin with greater elasticity was evident. The oedema was very slight and the oiliness was controllable. The general texture was softer and the colour was brighter and even. The client was aware of the changes and had received positive comments from colleagues which certainly added to her sense of well-being.

Throughout the last six years the monthly facial has varied, but biological peeling has been carried out very regularly and additional treatments have included aromatherapy.

Recently the client's skin changed dramatically and became excessively dry. The client also experienced fatigue. The therapist advised her to see her doctor and subsequent tests showed an underactive thyroid. The client now takes medication for this. It is interesting to note how quickly the skin reacts to bodily changes and is often the first warning that something is wrong.

51–60

CASE HISTORY 27

Abbie

Client   Abbie – female – Caucasian –
                                     Welsh

Age   52

Presenting problem   dehydrated facial skin

Previous history and medical history

The client's skin had become very dehydrated. She was a 'sun worshipper' and had sunbathed regularly throughout her life. The client's general health was good. She was a non-smoker and had a balanced, healthy diet. She was menopausal and was taking Hormone Replacement Therapy; otherwise she was taking no medication.

Points to check

- Health
- Menopause/hormones
- Diet
- Stress
- Sunbathing

Assessment of situation

The client's skin was severely dehydrated.

Microscopic analysis

The microscopic skin test showed a level of fatty acid slightly below normal and severe dehydration throughout the epidermic layers. The connective tissue was not in good condition, indicating that elastin and collagen had deteriorated.

*T*reatment plan

1 Monthly facial using specific products.
2 Homecare routine using specialised products and 'normalising' treatment – twice daily.
3 Six months later – microscopic facial retest.
4 Monthly facial for skin maintenance – ongoing.

After the initial analysis, specific products were recommended for treatment and the client had her first facial. This consisted of a deep cleanse, a biological exfoliation mask and a specialised 'normalising' treatment using a gel mask and a cream (the cream contains extracts from the sea, similar substances to our own body waters, which draw water from the dermis to the epidermis by osmosis). A lymphatic drainage massage followed and, finally, the client's skin was moisturised.

After each course of treatment had been completed, the client used a collagen cream and an elastin cream for daycare. The client followed a specific homecare routine, using a specialised cleanser and toner containing water-soluble essential oil and continuing the 'normalising' course of treatment. The client was also expected to use a high-factor sunblock to prevent further damage from the sun.

The salon treatment followed the same format for six months, after which a microscopic re-test was carried out. (At this point a change of treatment products could be recommended.)

*R*esults and follow-up

The client's skin showed considerable improvement after the six-month course of treatment and improved hydration was evident. The client continued to have a monthly maintenance facial, using the same specialised products. The programme is ongoing.

This microscopic, diagnostic analysis of the skin allows the therapist to 'see' the immediate problem and to be able to give an intensive treatment programme using substances that the skin requires at the time of assessment.

———

This is a **specialist treatment** *– refer to page 126 (microscopic analysis) for further details.*

CASE HISTORY 28

Donna

Client	Donna – female – Caucasian – English
Age	53
Presenting problem	dry, patchy, irritated skin on the face and neck, fluctuating throughout the month

Previous history and medical history

The client had been experiencing menopausal symptoms for three years; her monthly cycle was erratic. The skin was particularly sensitive prior to menstruation, and hormonal disturbances were clearly adding to, if not responsible for, the condition. The client had a relatively balanced diet and, until recently, had slept well. Sleep now tended to be broken by 'hot flushes'. Recently the client was experiencing intermittent depression and her skin was adding to this problem. The client's general health was good and, until menopause, the skin had responded well to a daily routine of cleansing, toning and moisturising. She was not taking any medication.

Points to check
- Endocrine and nervous systems
- Menopause
- Skin care routine
- Diet
- Stress
- Sleep pattern

*A*ssessment of situation

The client's skin was very sensitive because of the dryness. Some areas were dry, flaky and red. The skin was taut and dehydration was apparent over the entire face and neck areas. The client was very upset about her appearance.

*T*reatment plan

1 Facial every week for three weeks.
2 Homecare – use of aromatherapy oils three to four times a week and attention to diet.
3 Bath oils for depression/stress caused by menopause.
4 Monthly facial for four years – ongoing.

The client responded well to a mild cleanser and toner. Aromatherapy oils were used in a weakened solution so as to avoid any risk of irritation (which can be common with a dry skin). The oil selected was lavender and it was mixed with apricot kernel. A biological hydrating mask was used afterwards, followed by a light moisturiser (usual after this type of mask). The skin responded well to treatment – it appeared more even textured, the irritation was reduced and the dry, flakiness was dispersed. The facial was repeated every week for three weeks.

The client also used a solution of the same oils three to four times a week at home. In addition she paid attention to her diet to ensure it was balanced and that she was receiving adequate nutrients. A multi-vitamin supplement was taken.

After one month, the client's skin had a significantly improved appearance:

- even colour
- softer texture
- reduced dry patches

The redness/dryness continued to occur throughout the monthly cycle but it was lessened. It was apparent that the hormone changes were contributing to this factor. The client continued to have regular monthly facials and the aromatherapy oils were changed according to the condition of the skin at that time.

The client was encouraged to continue using oil at home, alternating aromatherapy oils with a bland oil, e.g. apricot kernel. The condition responded well to aromatherapy treatments and the client was therefore encouraged to use aromatherapy bath oils to assist the menopause. Suitable bath oils were rose alternating with sandalwood. Facial oils used throughout the treatment plan were lavender, jasmine and rose.

Results and follow-up

The client's general well-being improved after the first three treatments and the remaining four years of the menopause have been less difficult. The client continues to have a monthly aromatherapy facial and her skin has never regressed.

This study shows the importance of assisting the 'whole' person, rather than focusing solely on specific symptoms. It also demonstrates the effects that aromatherapy can have on the skin and the body – highlighting the physical and psychological benefits of this therapy.

───

Aromatherapy is a **specialist treatment** *– refer to page 127 for further details.*

CASE HISTORY 29

Tessa

Client	Tessa – female – Caucasian – Irish
Age	53
Presenting problem	fine hair growth on top lip and occasional hairs on chin – sensitive to treatment

Previous history and medical history

The client worked part-time as a physiotherapist's receptionist. She suffered with depression and had a chronic back problem caused by an accident several years ago. The back condition was being treated by the physiotherapist.

Ten years ago she had had an ovarian cyst removed. Seven years later she had a cyst removed from her breast. Two years ago she had commenced Hormone Replacement Therapy as she was suffering from hot flushes, but this was discontinued after six months as she felt it gave her migraine.

The client had had intermittent electrolysis for about three years prior to coming to this electrolysist for treatment.

Points to check

- Health problems
- Endocrine system
- Client's emotional condition and physical comfort

Assessment of situation

The client had fine hair growth on the top lip and chin. She was very sensitive to the electrical current and it was necessary to find a tolerance level.

*T*reatment plan

1 Five minutes every three to four weeks for two years.
2 Five minutes every seven to nine weeks for one year and continuing.
3 Homecare advice on hygiene of the area and skin care.

As the client's tolerance level was low, she always had a maximum of five minutes treatment and approximately only five hairs were removed at a session. It has been necessary to go slowly and to use as low a current as possible due to the client's low pain threshold.

*R*esults and follow-up

The client's hair growth is now very light. Each treatment is still for five minutes duration, but is now given every seven to nine weeks. The client's skin always responds well to treatment, showing only a little erythema which fades quickly.

The client has taken considerably longer to treat than the electrolysist originally envisaged, but the case shows how important it is to adjust treatment for the individual client.

CASE HISTORY 30

Tricia

Client   Tricia – female – Asian
Age   55
Presenting problem   mature skin with constant
                              eruptions on chin

Previous history and medical history

The client suffered with irritable bowel syndrome (IBS), believed medically
to be caused by the client's diet of hot, spicy food. Her general health was
moderate. She had had a hysterectomy two years earlier and was not taking
HRT. The client was taking no medication, unless IBS was a problem and
then she used medication (steroids). She chose to take these only if
absolutely necessary. The client's diet was high in fat, carbohydrates and
vegetables. She was a vegetarian and a very small eater. She had no desire to
change her diet. The client had a busy working life. She slept well, but sleep
was limited to six hours due to early rising.

The client had been suffering from spots for two months. She had never had
this problem before and was very concerned about it. She had been suffering
an IBS attack for several weeks. The client had a regular cleansing routine,
using natural-based products, and she used a light day moisturiser.

Points to check

- Medical
- Hormones
- Diet (eruptions on chin and/or around mouth often occur when there are
  bowel or intestinal problems)
- Stress
- Digestive and renal systems

*A*ssessment of situation

The client's skin was mature and had some dark pigment patches (she had lived in a hot country for several years). The texture was smooth, except for the chin area, and the colour was even. The elasticity of the skin was generally poor and muscle tone was poor, particularly around the jawline. There were a number of eruptions on the chin.

*T*reatment plan

> 1 Facial every two weeks for six weeks.
> 2 Facial every six to eight weeks over two years and continuing.
> 3 Homecare advice and routine.

The first facial commenced with deep cleansing. Direct High Frequency was then used for five minutes as a method of warming the face and also for its bactericidal effect on the chin. The skin responded instantly – it appeared brighter and there was evidence of increased circulation. The eruptions looked calmer. A pre-mask, Italian Mud, was used to stimulate, clear impurities and re-condition the skin. The skin responded well and glowed. There was also some improvement in the elasticity of the skin. Facial massage followed, with emphasis on muscle stimulation and lymphatic drainage. Aromatherapy creams were used containing jasmin oil. The total effect of this specialised facial was very encouraging for the client. There was evidence of increased muscle tone, and muscle testing showed a good response. The skin appeared firmer and brighter, and the eruptions were less noticeable – calmer and paler in colour. The client was pleased with the total look of her face.

The client was advised to include a mask in her homecare routine and to use jasmin cream as a nourishing cream and to improve elasticity. The client was also advised to include some light tapping movements (tapotement) around the jawline and cheeks to assist the muscles. The client was asked to consider a greater fluid intake, particularly water.

Two weeks later, the skin had maintained its improved even texture, but the elasticity and muscle tone still needed attention (although there had been some improvement). The eruptions were calm and only slightly visible. Electrical Muscle Stimulation was discussed, but the client declined. Her main aim was to eliminate the eruptions. The second facial followed a similar pattern to the first with the same good results. The increased circulation and muscular activity improved the skin's elasticity and the client saw this as a bonus, as the eruptions were barely visible.

By the third facial, two weeks later, there had been no new eruptions and there was no sign of the earlier ones. The client's IBS was also stable.

*R*esults and follow-up

The client has maintained regular facials every six to eight weeks and there has been a gradual improvement in skin colour and elasticity, and the skin appears firm and smooth.

There have been two occurrences of eruptions in the last two years, each lasting for about six weeks. These responded to Direct High Frequency and mud masks. The eruptions coincided with two severe attacks of irritable bowel syndrome, each lasting six to eight weeks. However, the irritable bowel syndrome has been more controllable. The client has considered her diet a little and water intake has been increased.

The client has maintained a regular homecare routine and followed the advice given. She is very pleased with the outcome and feels that she has seen the results of her own efforts as well as from beauty treatments.

This study shows the importance of having a good comprehension of the client's health problems (irritable bowel syndrome) and the relevance of the problems in relation to skin care.

———

Aromatherapy is a **specialist treatment** *– refer to page 127 for further details.*

CASE HISTORY 31

Elise

Client   Elise – female – Spanish

Age   58

Presenting problem   oedema, particularly in the eye
                              area and jawline, and loss of
                              skin tone

*P*revious history and medical history

The condition had developed over a period of time and the client's age
suggested general loss of skin tone.

The client's general health was good. She did have raised blood pressure, but
was not taking any medication. The client was in the menopause. She had no
previous history of skin disorders, but did have an allergy to coffee. She had
a varied diet and a relaxed life style.

*P*oints to check

- Endocrine system
- Renal
- Circulatory
- Digestive system

*A*ssessment of situation

The client's condition was probably age related, affected by circulatory
problems and menopausal changes. The skin was dehydrated and there was
considerable oedema in the eye area and jawline.

*T*reatment plan

> Facial every two weeks for 12 weeks.

Initially, an aromatherapy facial was given using a cool vaporiser with camomile and neroli essential oils. The skin responded well and was soft and fresh. There was slight erythema and slight change in oedema.

For the second facial, iontophoresis was used with plant extracts. The skin appeared cool and the texture was soft. There was a slight change in oedema.

The third facial was given using ionized royal jelly serum and manual lymphatic massage concentrating on the jawline. The results were excellent and there was a noticeable decrease in oedema.

For the fourth facial, royal jelly and related products were again used. Electrical lymphatic drainage was also considered and applied, particularly near the eye areas (as far as is safe to operate), on low pressure. There was a good result and considerable improvement, particularly to the oedema around the eyes.

The fifth treatment was the same as the fourth, but electrical lymphatic drainage was used in all major areas of the face. There was a marked *total* improvement and this was noticed by the client's friends.

The sixth facial consisted of electrical lymphatic drainage, followed by a full facial using collagen products. The skin appeared less puffy and much smoother. The tone had improved.

*R*esults and follow-up

The client was pleased with the results of treatment – her skin appeared less puffy and the overall tone had increased. She was advised to use a royal jelly cleanser, toner and night cream. She has done this and the positive effects from using the products were apparent.

The maintenance programme is a bi-weekly facial which will resume in the autumn and continue throughout the winter when the client is resident in this area.

This study shows that, although the client was experiencing menopause and there were some underlying circulatory problems, her facial skin responded to treatments which were compatible with her skin and her immediate symptoms. The short intensive treatment plan and the vital homecare routine contributed to the success of this client's treatment.

————

Aromatherapy is a **specialist treatment** *– see page 127 for further details.*

CASE HISTORY 32

Ingrid

Client   Ingrid – female – Caucasian – English

Age   59

Presenting problem   mature skin, dry, prone to itchiness and redness – sensitive to products

Previous history and medical history

The client had good general health, but had always had a delicate skin. She suffered with dermatitis on her hands throughout the winter months and her facial skin had become more sensitive since her hysterectomy ten years earlier. The client still had her ovaries. She was menopausal and experiencing hot flushes. The client enjoyed a pleasant, relaxed lifestyle, with regular sleep – seven hours – and her stress level was very low. She enjoyed a varied, balanced diet with a good fluid intake of water, coffee and occasional alcohol. Her cleansing routine had consisted of soap and water and a light moisturiser, but she had recently stopped using soap because it was causing irritation. The eye area was particularly sensitive.

Points to check

- Circulatory system
- Menopause symptoms
- Products/treatment of skin
- Sensitivity

Assessment of situation

The client's skin was mature and dehydrated. It was very pale, thin and sensitive, with noticeable capillaries. The client's harsh treatment of her skin was obviously affecting its texture, but menopausal problems (hot flushes) could also have been aggravating the situation. She had a red ring around the eyes and red eyelids. Although they looked sore, they only irritated when touched.

Treatment plan

1 Facial every week for four weeks.
2 Twice monthly facial.
3 Homecare routine.
4 Monthly maintenance facial.

The client responded well to gentle cleansing, toning and hand massage using a nourishing cream. The skin did react to touch by turning pink, but it never became too warm. This reaction reduced throughout the facial. Emollient masks for hydration were also used. After four facials the skin appeared more balanced and the capillaries were less noticeable. The eye area improved as the circulation improved and the client's skin no longer reacted to the products used.

A homecare routine was established at the beginning with the client using cream cleanser, mild toner, nourishing cream and daytime moisturiser.

Results and follow-up

Five years since the initial treatment the client's skin remains stable, but there have been occasions when the eyes have reacted – usually when the client was unwell or when she changed her eye make-up products. She continues to have a monthly maintenance facial.

This case study shows how quickly the skin can respond to treatment. The fact that the client was mature could have meant that the skin would have been very slow to respond and that some damage was more likely to occur.

CASE HISTORY 33

Irene

Client

Irene – female – Caucasian – South African

Age

60

Presenting problem

severe sun-damaged skin, hyperpigmentation and prolapsis of the facial tissues

Previous history and medical history

The client had lived in the South African Transvaal area for many years, living an outdoor life as a rancher. She had severely sun-damaged skin and had developed many skin cancers during the last ten years. These had been surgically removed, leaving behind hyperpigmentation and prolapsis of the facial tissues. No further information was available.

Points to check

- Medical
- General health
- Skin sensitivity
- Endocrine system

Assessment of situation

The client had severely sun-damaged skin, with hyperpigmentation and prolapsis of the facial tissues.

*T*reatment plan

1 Ten enzyme treatments.
2 Heavy, six-layer alpha-hydroxy treatment.
3 Melanoplex System treatment for pigmentation.
4 Homecare – daily cleansing routine and application of vitamin E oil and concentrated vitamin C protein cream.

The client's treatment commenced with ten enzyme treatments, followed by a heavy, six-layer alpha-hydroxy treatment. After the entire dead cell structure was hydrolyzed, the client underwent a series of pigmentation treatments called the Melanoplex System. This new treatment dissembles dark spots without bleaching and it contains no harmful substance (i.e. no hydroquinone).

The client was also provided with a home maintenance programme. This consists of daily cleansing with a low pH cleanser, followed by spraying with a special polarised mineral and herbal water. The water acts like the secretions from the sudiferous gland, which is the body's own moisturiser. Immediately afterwards she applies a mucilised vitamin E oil (represents the sebum from the sebaceous gland) which binds with the water and re-establishes the natural acid mantle, moist and protective. Finally, she applies a heavily concentrated vitamin C protein cream to stimulate her own collagen via the fibroblast cells, in order to produce healthy collagen. This is the major factor in the 'lift' or firming which results when treatment is complete.

*R*esults and follow-up

The client still has regular enzyme treatments at the clinic to maintain her improved appearance. She also wears transdermal sunblock FACTOR 30 when she is outdoors.

This study shows the amazing response the skin can make to this highly specialised treatment programme. (See Figures 1 and 2 on pages 122 and 123.)

———

This is a **specialist treatment** *– refer to page 122 (hydrolyzation treatment) for further details.*

61 and over

CASE HISTORY 34

Rosie

Client   Rosie – female – Caucasian –
                               English
Age   62
Presenting problem   sensitive, delicate, skin – prone
                               to erythema – with some
                               puffiness and fine lines

Previous history and medical history
No information was available.

Points to check
- Sensitivity
- Hormones
- Products
- Nervous renal and circulatory systems
- Heredity

Assessment of situation
The client showed signs of a nervous disposition. She had sensitive, delicate skin with some oedema and fine lines.

Treatment plan

| 1 Regular bi-monthly facials over a two-year period, including:
- electrical lymphatic drainage (very low intensity);
- aromatherapy facials;
- thermal revitalisation;
- collagen treatments.
2 Homecare routine. |

Cleansing and massage were performed lightly to avoid any aggravation of the skin. The client responded well to camomile products, so these were used initially for her cleansing treatment. Her face was massaged with an enriched cream and lymphatic electrical drainage was then given, followed by a camomile mask.

Successive facials used wheatgerm cream and rose and sandalwood aromatherapy oils, again followed by camomile masks. The client also had a thermalised revitalisation treatment, using a very low current as it was obviously important not to use heat on this skin. The skin responded well to this. Later facials used German collagen-based products. The client's skin was treated very carefully throughout.

Results and follow-up

The client's skin responded well to all the treatments. Electrical lymphatic drainage was particularly effective in reducing the puffiness of the skin, and the client also found this treatment to be very soothing. The aromatherapy facials gave a very soothing result, balancing the skin, and the collagen treatments re-moisturised the skin. The client has maintained a homecare routine using collagen-based products.

A noticeable feature of this case was that the client's general well-being also improved during treatment. Her response to the treatment programme has therefore been twofold – the facial condition has improved and the client's nervous tendency has responded positively.

———

Aromatherapy is a **specialist treatment** *– refer to page 127 for further details.*

CASE HISTORY 35

Kim

C*lient*	Kim – female – Caucasian – English
A*ge*	63 – retired
P*resenting problem*	terminal hair growth on face, neck (beard area) shoulders and upper body

Previous history and medical history

The client had had a benign tumour on the pituitary gland, which was successfully removed at age 58. The client showed signs of acromegaly – enlargement of the mandible, hands and feet. She was also suffering from mild diabetes, which was controlled by dietary means. In addition, she suffered from hypertension, which was medically controlled. She had regular check-ups with her doctor and attended hospital every three months for a check-up with her consultant. The distressing side effects of these problems were extensive terminal hair growth on her face and neck and very extensive dark growth on her shoulders and upper body. Her doctor was willing for her to undertake electrolysis treatment. Because of the extent of her problem and underlying conditions (high blood pressure and diabetes), the electrolysist decided to concentrate initially on the exposed areas – the face and neck.

Points to check

- Medical
- High blood pressure
- Diabetes
- Endocrine system

- Circulatory system
- Digestive system

*A*ssessment of situation

The client had extensive terminal hair growth on her face, neck, shoulders and upper body. Close medical liaison was vital regarding her conditions and poor healing due to diabetes.

*T*reatment plan

1 Exposed areas – 30 minutes every week for two and a half years (alternate areas treated to allow for slow healing).
2 Other areas – 30 minutes every two weeks for two and a half years, and continuing.

Treatment started with weekly 30-minute sessions, alternating the sites treated to allow adequate healing time (because of the poor healing of the skin associated with diabetes). The probes were spaced at twice the normal distance, 8mm (one-quarter inch) instead of 4mm (one-eighth inch), and progress was therefore very slow. However, because the client understood the importance of caution in order to prevent scarring, she became much more relaxed and her pain threshold improved.

After several months of treatment the area was mostly clear between treatments and regrowth was dealt with much more quickly. The client was advised to shave the area if regrowth was unacceptable and interfered with her social arrangements. Appointments were easily re-arranged to suit the client, as she was not working outside of the home.

*R*esults and follow-up

The facial hair was eliminated after approximately two and a half years. The client is now having the other areas treated but, because these are so extensive, it will take longer.

The financial commitment is also of relevance as the client is retired and receives no assistance from the health service. She accepts that electrolysis is part of her life and will be for sometime. She feels that this is worth it as she feels confident about her appearance again and is more able to enjoy life.

This client's hair problem developed as a result of treatment for her medical condition. This was very traumatic for the client, and it is encouraging to see that electrolysis was able to give her physical help and psychological reassurance.

CASE HISTORY 36

Jean

C*lient*   Jean – female – Caucasian –
                              English
A*ge*   67 – retired
P*resenting problem*   oily, coarse skin

P*revious history and medical history*

The client had experienced a problem with her skin for several years. She
came for treatment whilst resident in Spain but, as she only lived in this area
for a few months of each year, treatments were concentrated into a few
months when she could attend regularly. No further information was
available.

P*oints to check*

- Age
- Post-menopause
- Endocrine system

A*ssessment of situation*

The client's skin texture was coarse and she had an oily centre panel with
evidence of comedones. There was some hair growth on the upper lip.

*T*reatment plan

> 1 Fifteen treatments over two three-month periods in two years, consisting of:
> - deep cleansing;
> - galvanic desincrustation and comedone extraction;
> - biological peeling and vaporising;
> - massage;
> - mask containing seaweed extracts;
> - a single iontophoresis revitalising treatment.
> 2 Homecare routine.

At each treatment the client's skin was deep cleansed using products that were slightly astringent. Galvanic desincrustation and comedone extraction were then carried out. This was followed by biological peeling and vaporising, and, finally, a light massage and a mask containing nutritive seaweed extracts were applied. On one occasion, the client had an additional treatment of iontophoresis, using products for revitalising the skin.

*R*esults and follow-up

The results following treatment were always very good – the comedones were removed and the skin was brighter and improved in texture. In addition, the client followed a homecare routine, using a cleansing milk for normal skin with a witchhazel tonic and a cleansing gel for the oily panel.

This study shows that, with intensive treatments and a regular homecare routine, a good response is possible even if treatment is not carried out as ideally planned.

APPENDIX – SPECIALIST TREATMENTS

HYDROLYZATION TREATMENT

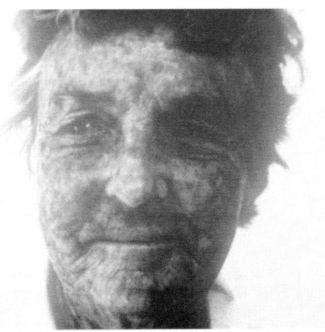

Figure 1 Severe hyperpigmentation

Case studies 13 (Susan), 18 (Jo) and 33 (Irene) have been submitted by the Danné Montague-King clinics in California, South Africa and Hong Kong. Danné Montague-King specialises in treatment for dehydrated skin, acne, hyperpigmentation and scarred skin. The treatments consist of:

1 removing dead and dying skin cells by hydrolyzation ('turning the dead cells into a weak acid' to get rid of them using enzyme and alpha-hydroxy treatments);
2 treating the remaining living cells with formulae to which they respond.

Figure 2 Successful treatment using alpha-hydroxy acid and melanoplex treatments

Danné Montague-King explains the treatments and how they are conducted:

After dead and dying cells have been removed via professional treatments and the proper homecare regime (usually a modified version of the professional treatments), the skin then requires daily applications of formulae it will respond *positively* to. This means a morning and evening cleansing with a low pH (acid) cleanser that contains natural surfactants (sudsing agents), usually procured from soap barks, cactus plants and other herbal agents. This type of cleanser must also contain a natural bactricide that will destroy gram-positive and gram-negative bacteria in the skin.

The next aim is to replicate the skin's protective acid mantle. The acid mantle is naturally manufactured by the sweat and oil glands of the skin and flows evenly over the surface during youth. Thick build-up from dead cells and alkaline residue left over from using common soaps actually prohibit these two vital secretions from establishing the protective layer. As this layer is slightly acid, lack of it will result in sallow, dull, dark-looking skin with hyper-spotty pigmentation.

It is possible to re-establish this acid mantle immediately after cleansing by spraying the face with water that contains carefully balanced herbs and minerals. After spraying this type of water over the face and neck, a thin, fractionated oil, preferably vitamin E based, should be massaged in with the water. This will create an exact duplicate of the acid mantle and bind water into the skin for hours. Water is the only true moisturiser and most creams sold on the market are not water soluble.

After replacing the acid mantle, the next step would be to use a water-soluble cream made of protein (such as soy). This should contain the full range of essential amino acids that living cells need, thus retarding the ageing process. For oriental skin, this cream should have a low pH and contain a sun screen and ascorbic acid (vitamin C). Vitamin C is the most important vitamin for the production of new collagen in the skin via the fibroblast cell. Animal collagen does not last in the skin, even with injections, because the body will not accept the hydrolyzed animal-cell blueprint from an outside source. We can, however, aid the production of new cells. Topically applied vitamin C is important in this production. Oral doses in excess of two thousand per day are now medically recommended in the USA, not only for internal help in propagating new collagen but also for assisting the immune system. Collagen cells (or fibres) are the cells that keep the skin tight and firm.

Alpha-hydroxy acids

Alpha-hydroxy acids are hydrolytic acids. They can be very effective in removing dead cells from Asian and Oriental skins, because they pull moisture into the upper strata or dead cells which in turn swell up like miniature balloons and burst, with the fragments detaching from the skin. Glycolic acid, processed from sugar cane, seems to be the most popular of the alpha-hydroxy acids. Our research in the Danné Montague-King clinics suggests, however, that glycolic acid is the least predictable and the most uncontrollably caustic of all available alpha-hydroxy acids. We prefer a blend of malic acid, lactic acid and citric acids (to help build collagen), with just a small percentage of glycolic acid – enough to break the alkaline build-up on the skin's surface, but not enough to cause trauma and hyper-spotty pigmentation. We have had overwhelming success with this methodology from Hong Kong to Taiwan and all through the Pacific rim. Some removals of dark spots, acne lesions and superficial scars have been amazing.

Melanoplex

A series of melanoplex treatments would normally be applied directly to any dark areas remaining after the alpha-hydroxy acid treatment. Melanoplex serums and creams are a new formulation of skin-lightening agents that do not contain the controversial and damaging ingredient hydroquinone. Hydroquinone has been banned from use in cosmetics in any formulation over 2% in most developed countries of the world. The breakthrough of melanoplex will aid many people of all colours in maintaining a perfect, even skin tone.

Sunblock SPF 30

In addition, because the sun is no longer kind to even the darkest skin (due to free radicals in the atmosphere and ozone depletion), every client undergoing the professional treatments described must wear at least a 30 SPF sunblock daily. In Australia it is compulsory for all school children to be sunblocked during daylight hours. A water soluble cream sunblock with very little oil has been found to be best, particularly if the wearer has to put it on over other home prescriptives and then wear make-up. This transdermal type of sunblock is, however, made by very few companies due to lack of understanding of how the skin chemistry works. The Danné Montague-King clinics manufacture this for our international clients.

MICROSCOPIC ANALYSIS

Figure 3 Microscopic analysis showing damage to the connective tissue after extensive use of soap and water

Figure 4 The connective fibres are regenerating after a three month normalisation programme

Case studies 20 (Louise) and 27 (Abbie) have been submitted by June Massie. June specialises in using microscopic analysis in order to make an assessment of the skin.

The process involves taking a test of the skin which enables the skin's moisture and oil levels to be assessed. This process is carried out on the epidermis *before* the skin is cleansed. The test uses three coloured reagents (similar to litmus). Two reagents measure the fatty acid of the skin and one reagent measures the moisture level of the skin. All three tests require the skin to be wiped with a drop of reagent on sterile cotton wool. The colour changes that occur are checked with an analysis chart.

A further investigation of the skin can be carried out which assesses the internal structure and condition of the dermis, measuring the elastin and collagen. A latex solution is applied to a small area of skin. When it has dried, it is peeled off and varnish is applied to the latex. A varnished print can then be removed when it has dried. It is then ready for microscopic analysis.

These tests allow the most appropriate creams and solutions to be suggested. Re-testing of the skin can take place after a suitable treatment period.

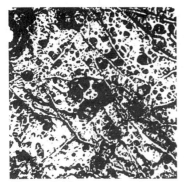

Figure 5 Microscopic analysis showing a very oily, unbalanced skin

Figure 6 Microscopic analysis showing skin with a good hydration level

AROMATHERAPY TREATMENT

Case studies 10 (Frances), 12 (Melanie), 16 (Jane), 28 (Donna), 30 (Tricia), 31 (Elise) and 34 (Rosie) include aromatherapy treatments. Aromatherapy is the use of pure essential oils for face and body therapy. The aromatherapist requires an in-depth knowledge of the qualities of essential oils and experience with mixing and using the oils for a treatment programme.

Essential oils are extremely volatile substances. They are the life force or vital elements of a plant. They are considered to be vegetable hormones. They are extracted from leaves, flowers, roots and bark. Very little of the actual essential oil needs to be added to a carrier oil for massage purposes.

Essential oils are absorbed through the skin into the blood stream. This can take between 20 and 70 minutes. They affect the individual's physiological and psychological state. Essential oils have many individual qualities but most of them have some general effects:

- they encourage the growth of new cells;
- they have an anti-bacterial action;
- they accelerate toxic elimination;
- they increase the elasticity of the skin;
- they create well-being.

When used in facial treatments, it is not only necessary for the aromatherapist to be skilled in a range of oils, but also to be able to select the appropriate oil for treatment. Although the client can benefit from a single treatment, the aromatherapist should be skilled in developing a treatment programme or combining aromatherapy with other treatments in order for them to complement each other and be effective.